A Family Fun Workbook of Quotes for Children of all Ages

Sandy Hoberman

Technics Publications

Technics Publications, LLC
115 Linda Vista, Sedona, AZ 86336 USA
https://www.TechnicsPub.com

First Printing 2023
Copyright © 2023 by Sandy Hoberman

ISBN, print ed.   9781634621632
ISBN, Kindle ed.   9781634621649
ISBN, ePub ed.   9781634621656

To my grandchildren:

Sadie, Sammy, Jamie, Spencer, Rebeka, Skyler, and David.

You have to believe in yourself

when no one else does.

Serena Williams

What does this quote mean?

_____

_____

_____

_____

Do you agree?

_____

_____

_____

_____

Create your own quote using your own thoughts.

_____

_____

_____

_____

Learn from yesterday,

live for today,

hope for tomorrow.

Albert Einstein

What does this quote mean?

_____

_____

_____

_____

Do you agree?

_____

_____

_____

_____

Create your own quote using your own thoughts.

_____

_____

_____

_____

Those who wish to sing will always find a song.

Swedish Proverb

What does this quote mean?

_____

_____

_____

_____

Do you agree?

_____

_____

_____

_____

Create your own quote using your own thoughts.

_____

_____

_____

_____

A new baby is like the beginning

of all things wonder,

hope,

a dream of possibilities.

Eda Leshan

What does this quote mean?

_____

_____

_____

_____

Do you agree?

_____

_____

_____

_____

Create your own quote using your own thoughts.

_____

_____

_____

_____

Life isn't about finding yourself.

Life is about creating yourself.

George Bernard Shaw

What does this quote mean?

_____

_____

_____

_____

Do you agree?

_____

_____

_____

_____

Create your own quote using your own thoughts.

_____

_____

_____

_____

When you reach the end of your rope,

tie a knot in it and hang on.

Franklin D. Roosevelt

What does this quote mean?

_____

_____

_____

_____

Do you agree?

_____

_____

_____

_____

Create your own quote using your own thoughts.

_____

_____

_____

_____

Today a reader,

tomorrow a leader.

Margaret Fuller

What does this quote mean?

_____

_____

_____

_____

Do you agree?

_____

_____

_____

_____

Create your own quote using your own thoughts.

_____

_____

_____

_____

I am not afraid of storms,

for I am learning how to sail my ship.

Louisa May Alcott

What does this quote mean?

_____

_____

_____

_____

Do you agree?

_____

_____

_____

_____

Create your own quote using your own thoughts.

_____

_____

_____

_____

No legacy is so rich as honesty.

William Shakespeare

What does this quote mean?

_____

_____

_____

_____

Do you agree?

_____

_____

_____

_____

Create your own quote using your own thoughts.

_____

_____

_____

_____

Talk to yourself like you would to someone you love.

Brené Brown

What does this quote mean?

_____

_____

_____

_____

Do you agree?

_____

_____

_____

_____

Create your own quote using your own thoughts.

_____

_____

_____

_____

Love is a fruit in season at all times,

and within reach of every hand.

Mother Teresa

What does this quote mean?

_____

_____

_____

_____

Do you agree?

_____

_____

_____

_____

Create your own quote using your own thoughts.

_____

_____

_____

_____

Nothing can dim the light which shines from within.

Maya Angelou

What does this quote mean?

_____

_____

_____

_____

Do you agree?

_____

_____

_____

_____

Create your own quote using your own thoughts.

_____

_____

_____

_____

What lies behind us and what lies before us

are tiny matters compared to what lies within us.

Ralph Waldo Emerson

What does this quote mean?

_____

_____

_____

_____

Do you agree?

_____

_____

_____

_____

Create your own quote using your own thoughts.

_____

_____

_____

_____

I am where I am because I believe in all possibilities.

Whoopi Goldberg

What does this quote mean?

_____

_____

_____

_____

Do you agree?

_____

_____

_____

_____

Create your own quote using your own thoughts.

_____

_____

_____

_____

There is always light,

if only we're brave enough to see it;

if only we're brave enough to be it.

Amanda Gorman

What does this quote mean?

_____

_____

_____

_____

Do you agree?

_____

_____

_____

_____

Create your own quote using your own thoughts.

_____

_____

_____

_____

You can find magic wherever you look.

Sit back and relax all you need is a book.

Dr. Seuss

What does this quote mean?

_____

_____

_____

_____

Do you agree?

_____

_____

_____

_____

Create your own quote using your own thoughts.

_____

_____

_____

_____

There will be an answer, let it be.

The Beatles

What does this quote mean?

_____

_____

_____

_____

Do you agree?

_____

_____

_____

_____

Create your own quote using your own thoughts.

_____

_____

_____

_____

Know who you are.

What other people think of you

is none of your business.

Grandpa Stu

What does this quote mean?

_____

_____

_____

_____

Do you agree?

_____

_____

_____

_____

Create your own quote using your own thoughts.

_____

_____

_____

_____

You have to trust in something –

your gut, destiny, life, karma, whatever.

This approach has never let me down,

and it has made all the difference in my life.

Steve Jobs

What does this quote mean?

_____

_____

_____

_____

Do you agree?

_____

_____

_____

_____

Create your own quote using your own thoughts.

_____

_____

_____

_____

My mission in life is not merely to survive,

but to thrive;

and to do so with some passion,

some compassion,

some humor,

and some style.

Maya Angelou

What does this quote mean?

_____

_____

_____

_____

Do you agree?

_____

_____

_____

_____

Create your own quote using your own thoughts.

_____

_____

_____

_____

Life is like riding a bicycle.

To keep your balance you must keep moving.

Albert Einstein

What does this quote mean?

_____

_____

_____

_____

Do you agree?

_____

_____

_____

_____

Create your own quote using your own thoughts.

_____

_____

_____

_____

"What day is it?" asked Pooh.

"It's today," squeaked Piglet.

"My favorite day," said Pooh.

A.A. Milne

What does this quote mean?

_____

_____

_____

_____

Do you agree?

_____

_____

_____

_____

Create your own quote using your own thoughts.

_____

_____

_____

_____

We don't see things as they are;

we see them as we are.

Anaïs Nin

What does this quote mean?

_____

_____

_____

_____

Do you agree?

_____

_____

_____

_____

Create your own quote using your own thoughts.

_____

_____

_____

_____

Music gives soul to the universe

and wings to the mind.

Plato

What does this quote mean?

_____

_____

_____

_____

Do you agree?

_____

_____

_____

_____

Create your own quote using your own thoughts.

_____

_____

_____

_____

No one can make you feel inferior

without your consent.

Eleanor Roosevelt

What does this quote mean?

_____

_____

_____

_____

Do you agree?

_____

_____

_____

_____

Create your own quote using your own thoughts.

_____

_____

_____

_____

Remember that sometimes not getting

what you want is a wonderful stroke of luck.

Dalai Lama

What does this quote mean?

_____

_____

_____

_____

Do you agree?

_____

_____

_____

_____

Create your own quote using your own thoughts.

_____

_____

_____

_____

Do or do not.

There is no try.

Yoda

What does this quote mean?

_____

_____

_____

_____

Do you agree?

_____

_____

_____

_____

Create your own quote using your own thoughts.

_____

_____

_____

_____

Everyone is a genius.

But if you judge a fish by its ability to climb a tree,

it will live its whole life believing that it is stupid.

Albert Einstein

What does this quote mean?

_____

_____

_____

_____

Do you agree?

_____

_____

_____

_____

Create your own quote using your own thoughts.

_____

_____

_____

_____

To succeed in life,

you need three things:

a wishbone,

a backbone,

and a funny bone.

Reba McEntire

What does this quote mean?

_____

_____

_____

_____

Do you agree?

_____

_____

_____

_____

Create your own quote using your own thoughts.

_____

_____

_____

_____

The best is yet to be.

Robert Browning

What does this quote mean?

_____

_____

_____

_____

Do you agree?

_____

_____

_____

_____

Create your own quote using your own thoughts.

_____

_____

_____

_____

Every strike brings me closer to the next home run.

Babe Ruth

What does this quote mean?

_____

_____

_____

_____

Do you agree?

_____

_____

_____

_____

Create your own quote using your own thoughts.

_____

_____

_____

_____

Grant me the serenity

to accept the things I cannot change,

courage to change the things I can,

and wisdom to know the difference.

Winnifred Crane Wygal

What does this quote mean?

_____

_____

_____

_____

Do you agree?

_____

_____

_____

_____

Create your own quote using your own thoughts.

_____

_____

_____

_____

I think that I shall never see

A poem lovely as a tree.

Joyce Kilmer

What does this quote mean?

_____

_____

_____

_____

Do you agree?

_____

_____

_____

_____

Create your own quote using your own thoughts.

_____

_____

_____

_____

Do not judge me by my successes,

judge me by how many times I fell down

and got back up again.

Nelson Mandela

What does this quote mean?

_____

_____

_____

_____

Do you agree?

_____

_____

_____

_____

Create your own quote using your own thoughts.

_____

_____

_____

_____

You have brains in your head.

You have feet in your shoes.

You can steer yourself any direction you choose.

You're on your own.

And you know what you know.

And you are the one who'll decide where to go.

Dr. Seuss

What does this quote mean?

_____

_____

_____

_____

Do you agree?

_____

_____

_____

_____

Create your own quote using your own thoughts.

_____

_____

_____

_____

Chance is always powerful.

Let your hook be always cast;

in the pool where you least expect it,

there will be a fish.

Ovid, Heroides

What does this quote mean?

_____

_____

_____

_____

Do you agree?

_____

_____

_____

_____

Create your own quote using your own thoughts.

_____

_____

_____

_____

The only way to do great work

is to love what you do.

Steve Jobs

What does this quote mean?

_____

_____

_____

_____

Do you agree?

_____

_____

_____

_____

Create your own quote using your own thoughts.

_____

_____

_____

_____

I've learned that people will forget what you said,

people will forget what you did,

but people will never forget

how you made them feel.

Maya Angelou

What does this quote mean?

_____

_____

_____

_____

Do you agree?

_____

_____

_____

_____

Create your own quote using your own thoughts.

_____

_____

_____

_____

When I listen to my inner self,

I hear the answers I need.

Louise Hay

What does this quote mean?

_____

_____

_____

_____

Do you agree?

_____

_____

_____

_____

Create your own quote using your own thoughts.

_____

_____

_____

_____

We can complain because rose bushes have thorns,

or rejoice because thorn bushes have roses.

Abraham Lincoln

What does this quote mean?

_____

_____

_____

_____

Do you agree?

_____

_____

_____

_____

Create your own quote using your own thoughts.

_____

_____

_____

_____

We are the hero of our own story.

Mary McCarthy

What does this quote mean?

_____

_____

_____

_____

Do you agree?

_____

_____

_____

_____

Create your own quote using your own thoughts.

_____

_____

_____

_____

And the day came when the risk to remain tight

in a bud was more painful

than the risk it took to blossom.

Anais Nin

What does this quote mean?

_____

_____

_____

_____

Do you agree?

_____

_____

_____

_____

Create your own quote using your own thoughts.

_____

_____

_____

_____

Passion is energy.

Feel the power that comes from

focusing on what excites you.

Oprah Winfrey

What does this quote mean?

_____

_____

_____

_____

Do you agree?

_____

_____

_____

_____

Create your own quote using your own thoughts.

_____

_____

_____

_____

Choosing to be positive

and having a grateful attitude

is going to determine

how you're going to live your life.

Joel Osteen

What does this quote mean?

_____

_____

_____

_____

Do you agree?

_____

_____

_____

_____

Create your own quote using your own thoughts.

_____

_____

_____

_____

What you think, you become.

What you feel, you attract.

What you imagine, you create.

Buddha

What does this quote mean?

_____

_____

_____

_____

Do you agree?

_____

_____

_____

_____

Create your own quote using your own thoughts.

_____

_____

_____

_____

Be happy with what you have

while working for what you want.

Hellen Keller

What does this quote mean?

_____

_____

_____

_____

Do you agree?

_____

_____

_____

_____

Create your own quote using your own thoughts.

_____

_____

_____

_____

Some people dance in the rain.

Others just get wet.

Dolly Parton

What does this quote mean?

_____

_____

_____

_____

Do you agree?

_____

_____

_____

_____

Create your own quote using your own thoughts.

_____

_____

_____

_____

80 percent of success in life is just showing up.

Woody Allen

What does this quote mean?

_____

_____

_____

_____

Do you agree?

_____

_____

_____

_____

Create your own quote using your own thoughts.

_____

_____

_____

_____

It's kind of fun to do the impossible.

Walt Disney

What does this quote mean?

_____

_____

_____

_____

Do you agree?

_____

_____

_____

_____

Create your own quote using your own thoughts.

_____

_____

_____

_____

If you want to fly,

you have to give up the things that weigh you down.

Tony Morrison

What does this quote mean?

_____

_____

_____

_____

Do you agree?

_____

_____

_____

_____

Create your own quote using your own thoughts.

_____

_____

_____

_____

"Weeds are flowers too,

once you get to know them," said Pooh.

A.A. Milne

What does this quote mean?

_____

_____

_____

_____

Do you agree?

_____

_____

_____

_____

Create your own quote using your own thoughts.

_____

_____

_____

_____

People are often unreasonable, illogical, and self-centered. Forgive them anyway.

If you are kind, people may accuse you of selfish ulterior motives. Be kind anyway.

If you are successful, you will win some false friends and some true enemies. Succeed anyway.

If you are honest and frank, people may cheat you. Be honest and frank anyway.

What you spend years building, someone could destroy overnight. Build anyway.

If you find serenity and happiness, they may be jealous. Be happy anyway.

The good you do today, people will often forget tomorrow. Do good anyway.

Give the world the best you have, and it may never be enough. Give the best you've got anyway.

You see, in the final analysis it is between you and God; it was never between you and them anyway.

Mother Teresa

What does this quote mean?

_____

_____

_____

_____

Do you agree?

_____

_____

_____

_____

Create your own quote using your own thoughts.

_____

_____

_____

_____

You gain strength, courage, and confidence

by every experience in which you really stop

to look fear in the face.

You are able to say to yourself,

"I have lived through this horror.

I can take the next thing that comes along."

You must do the thing you think you cannot do.

Eleanor Roosevelt

What does this quote mean?

_____

_____

_____

_____

Do you agree?

_____

_____

_____

_____

Create your own quote using your own thoughts.

_____

_____

_____

_____

I find that the harder I work,

the more luck I seem to have.

Thomas Jefferson

What does this quote mean?

_____

_____

_____

_____

Do you agree?

_____

_____

_____

_____

Create your own quote using your own thoughts.

_____

_____

_____

_____

Think of yourself as on the threshold

of unparalleled success.

A whole, clear, glorious life lies before you.

Andrew Carnegie

What does this quote mean?

_____

_____

_____

_____

Do you agree?

_____

_____

_____

_____

Create your own quote using your own thoughts.

_____

_____

_____

_____

Whatever you can do or dream you can,

begin it;

Boldness has genius, power, and magic in it.

Johann Wolfgang Van Goethe

What does this quote mean?

_____

_____

_____

_____

Do you agree?

_____

_____

_____

_____

Create your own quote using your own thoughts.

_____

_____

_____

_____

Tell me and I forget.

Teach me and I remember.

Involve me and I learn.

Benjamin Franklin

What does this quote mean?

_____

_____

_____

_____

Do you agree?

_____

_____

_____

_____

Create your own quote using your own thoughts.

_____

_____

_____

_____

Tomorrow will be a better day.

Grandma Dotty Hoberman

What does this quote mean?

_____

_____

_____

_____

Do you agree?

_____

_____

_____

_____

Create your own quote using your own thoughts.

_____

_____

_____

_____

Two roads diverged in a wood, and I—

I took the one less traveled by,

And that has made all the difference.

Robert Frost

What does this quote mean?

_____

_____

_____

_____

Do you agree?

_____

_____

_____

_____

Create your own quote using your own thoughts.

_____

_____

_____

_____

Our greatest weakness lies in giving up.

The most certain way to succeed

is always to try just one more time.

Thomas Edison

What does this quote mean?

_____

_____

_____

_____

Do you agree?

_____

_____

_____

_____

Create your own quote using your own thoughts.

_____

_____

_____

_____

You're off to Great Places!

Today is your day!

Your mountain is waiting,

So... get on your way!

And will you succeed?

Yes you will indeed! (98 and 3/4 percent guaranteed.)

Be who you are and say what you feel,

because in the end those who matter don't mind

and those who mind don't matter.

Dr. Seuss

What does this quote mean?

_____

_____

_____

_____

Do you agree?

_____

_____

_____

_____

Create your own quote using your own thoughts.

_____

_____

_____

_____

If you change the way you look at things,

the things you look at change.

Wayne Dyer

What does this quote mean?

_____

_____

_____

_____

Do you agree?

_____

_____

_____

_____

Create your own quote using your own thoughts.

_____

_____

_____

_____

I saw the angel in the marble

and carved until I set her free.

Michelangelo

What does this quote mean?

_____

_____

_____

_____

Do you agree?

_____

_____

_____

_____

Create your own quote using your own thoughts.

_____

_____

_____

_____

Things have a way of working out.

Stu Hoberman

What does this quote mean?

_____

_____

_____

_____

Do you agree?

_____

_____

_____

_____

Create your own quote using your own thoughts.

_____

_____

_____

_____

Don't cry because it's over.

Smile because it happened.

Dr. Seuss

What does this quote mean?

_____

_____

_____

_____

Do you agree?

_____

_____

_____

_____

Create your own quote using your own thoughts.

_____

_____

_____

_____

There is only one success –

to be able to spend your life in your own way.

Christopher Morley

What does this quote mean?

_____

_____

_____

_____

Do you agree?

_____

_____

_____

_____

Create your own quote using your own thoughts.

_____

_____

_____

_____

The art of conversation lies in listening.

Malcolm Forbes

What does this quote mean?

_____

_____

_____

_____

Do you agree?

_____

_____

_____

_____

Create your own quote using your own thoughts.

_____

_____

_____

_____

If you hear a voice within you say

"you cannot paint," then by all means paint,

and that voice will be silenced.

Vincent Van Gogh

What does this quote mean?

_____

_____

_____

_____

Do you agree?

_____

_____

_____

_____

Create your own quote using your own thoughts.

_____

_____

_____

_____

You can do anything you want,

but you have to really, really Want.

Grandma Rae Goldstein

What does this quote mean?

_____

_____

_____

_____

Do you agree?

_____

_____

_____

_____

Create your own quote using your own thoughts.

_____

_____

_____

_____

Laughter is timeless.

Imagination has no age.

And dreams are forever.

Walt Disney

What does this quote mean?

_____

_____

_____

_____

Do you agree?

_____

_____

_____

_____

Create your own quote using your own thoughts.

_____

_____

_____

_____

They do me wrong who say I come no more

When once I knock and fail to find you in;

For every day I stand outside your door

And bid you wake and rise to fight and win.

Walter Malone

(Grandpa Lou's favorite quote)

What does this quote mean?

_____

_____

_____

_____

Do you agree?

_____

_____

_____

_____

Create your own quote using your own thoughts.

_____

_____

_____

_____

There is a voice inside of you

That whispers all day long,

"I feel this is right for me,

I know that this is wrong."

No teacher, preacher, parent, friend

Or wise man can decide

What's right for you--just listen to

The voice that speaks inside.

Shel Silverstein

What does this quote mean?

_____

_____

_____

_____

Do you agree?

_____

_____

_____

_____

Create your own quote using your own thoughts.

_____

_____

_____

_____

All you need is love.

But a little chocolate now and then doesn't hurt.

Charles Schulz

What does this quote mean?

_____

_____

_____

_____

Do you agree?

_____

_____

_____

_____

Create your own quote using your own thoughts.

_____

_____

_____

_____

Imagination is everything.

It is the preview of life's coming attractions.

Albert Einstein

What does this quote mean?

_____

_____

_____

_____

Do you agree?

_____

_____

_____

_____

Create your own quote using your own thoughts.

_____

_____

_____

_____

You cannot always control what goes on outside.

But you can always control what goes on inside.

Wayne Dyer

What does this quote mean?

_____

_____

_____

_____

Do you agree?

_____

_____

_____

_____

Create your own quote using your own thoughts.

_____

_____

_____

_____

The way I see it,

if you want the rainbow,

you gotta put up with the rain.

Dolly Parton

What does this quote mean?

_____

_____

_____

_____

Do you agree?

_____

_____

_____

_____

Create your own quote using your own thoughts.

_____

_____

_____

_____

Whether you think you can,

or you think you can't--you're right.

Henry Ford

What does this quote mean?

_____

_____

_____

_____

Do you agree?

_____

_____

_____

_____

Create your own quote using your own thoughts.

_____

_____

_____

_____

To handle yourself, use your head.

To handle others, use your heart.

Eleanor Roosevelt

What does this quote mean?

_____

_____

_____

_____

Do you agree?

_____

_____

_____

_____

Create your own quote using your own thoughts.

_____

_____

_____

_____

"How do you spell 'love'?" - Piglet

"You don't spell it...you feel it." - Pooh

A.A. Milne

What does this quote mean?

_____

_____

_____

_____

Do you agree?

_____

_____

_____

_____

Create your own quote using your own thoughts.

_____

_____

_____

_____

Just as ripples spread out when a single pebble

is dropped into water,

the actions of individuals

can have far-reaching effects.

Dalai Lama

What does this quote mean?

_____

_____

_____

_____

Do you agree?

_____

_____

_____

_____

Create your own quote using your own thoughts.

_____

_____

_____

_____

The best way to cheer yourself up

is to try to cheer somebody else up.

Mark Twain

What does this quote mean?

_____

_____

_____

_____

Do you agree?

_____

_____

_____

_____

Create your own quote using your own thoughts.

_____

_____

_____

_____

As you think so shall you be.

Wayne Dyer

What does this quote mean?

_____

_____

_____

_____

Do you agree?

_____

_____

_____

_____

Create your own quote using your own thoughts.

_____

_____

_____

_____

The price of greatness is responsibility.

Winston Churchill

What does this quote mean?

_____

_____

_____

_____

Do you agree?

_____

_____

_____

_____

Create your own quote using your own thoughts.

_____

_____

_____

_____

If your actions create a legacy

that inspires others to dream more,

learn more,

do more and become more, then,

you are an excellent leader.

Dolly Parton

What does this quote mean?

_____

_____

_____

_____

Do you agree?

_____

_____

_____

_____

Create your own quote using your own thoughts.

_____

_____

_____

_____

A man is a success if he gets up in the morning

and goes to bed at night

and in between does what he wants to do.

Bob Dylan

What does this quote mean?

_____

_____

_____

_____

Do you agree?

_____

_____

_____

_____

Create your own quote using your own thoughts.

_____

_____

_____

_____

"I think I can, I think I can, I think I can,"

puffed the little locomotive.

Platt & Munk

What does this quote mean?

_____

_____

_____

_____

Do you agree?

_____

_____

_____

_____

Create your own quote using your own thoughts.

_____

_____

_____

_____

Above all else, preparation is the key to success.

Alexander Graham Bell

What does this quote mean?

_____

_____

_____

_____

Do you agree?

_____

_____

_____

_____

Create your own quote using your own thoughts.

_____

_____

_____

_____

To Thine Own Self Be True.

William Shakespeare

What does this quote mean?

_____

_____

_____

_____

Do you agree?

_____

_____

_____

_____

Create your own quote using your own thoughts.

_____

_____

_____

_____

There is nothing in the world so irresistibly

contagious as laughter and good-humour.

Charles Dickens

What does this quote mean?

_____

_____

_____

_____

Do you agree?

_____

_____

_____

_____

Create your own quote using your own thoughts.

_____

_____

_____

_____

"I do not like green eggs and ham!

I do not like them, Sam-I-Am."

"You do not like them. So you say.

Try them! Try them!

And you may. Try them and you may, I say."

Dr. Seuss

What does this quote mean?

_____

_____

_____

_____

Do you agree?

_____

_____

_____

_____

Create your own quote using your own thoughts.

_____

_____

_____

_____

A journey of a thousand miles

begins with a single step.

Lao Tzu

What does this quote mean?

_____

_____

_____

_____

Do you agree?

_____

_____

_____

_____

Create your own quote using your own thoughts.

_____

_____

_____

_____

What you do today can improve all your tomorrows.

Ralph Marston

What does this quote mean?

_____

_____

_____

_____

Do you agree?

_____

_____

_____

_____

Create your own quote using your own thoughts.

_____

_____

_____

_____

As you think so shall you be.

Wayne Dyer

What does this quote mean?

_____

_____

_____

_____

Do you agree?

_____

_____

_____

_____

Create your own quote using your own thoughts.

_____

_____

_____

_____

Leadership and learning

are indispensable to each other.

John F. Kennedy

What does this quote mean?

_____

_____

_____

_____

Do you agree?

_____

_____

_____

_____

Create your own quote using your own thoughts.

_____

_____

_____

_____

Music produces a kind of pleasure

that human nature cannot do without.

Confucius

What does this quote mean?

_____

_____

_____

_____

Do you agree?

_____

_____

_____

_____

Create your own quote using your own thoughts.

_____

_____

_____

_____

Try to be a rainbow in someone's cloud.

Maya Angel

What does this quote mean?

_____

_____

_____

_____

Do you agree?

_____

_____

_____

_____

Create your own quote using your own thoughts.

_____

_____

_____

_____

Don't worry about a thing

'Cause every little thing gonna be alright.

Bob Marley

What does this quote mean?

_____

_____

_____

_____

Do you agree?

_____

_____

_____

_____

Create your own quote using your own thoughts.

_____

_____

_____

_____

Setting goals is the first step

in turning the invisible into the visible.

Tony Robbins

What does this quote mean?

_____

_____

_____

_____

Do you agree?

_____

_____

_____

_____

Create your own quote using your own thoughts.

_____

_____

_____

_____

In the adaptability and ease with which we experience change lies our happiness and freedom.

Buddha

What does this quote mean?

_____

_____

_____

_____

Do you agree?

_____

_____

_____

_____

Create your own quote using your own thoughts.

_____

_____

_____

_____

There are only two ways to live your life.

One is as though nothing is a miracle.

The other is as though everything is a miracle.

Albert Einstein

What does this quote mean?

_____

_____

_____

_____

Do you agree?

_____

_____

_____

_____

Create your own quote using your own thoughts.

_____

_____

_____

_____

Write down three things you are grateful for

before you go to sleep at night.

Read them again when you get up

in the morning and SMILE.

HAVE A GREAT DAY.

AND KNOW THAT I LOVE YOU.

Grandma's Quote

What does this quote mean?

_____

_____

_____

_____

Do you agree?

_____

_____

_____

_____

Create your own quote using your own thoughts.

_____

_____

_____

_____